A fan is hurt. We all rush towards him with the medics.

We must get him out.

All of a sudden a man gets up. He is in a foul mood. He looks at the goalkeeper and yells at him in a temper.

He picks up a coin and hurls it towards the keeper!

The coin hits the keeper hard, and he falls down with his hand at his head, in real pain.

He is hurt and has a bad cut on his head.

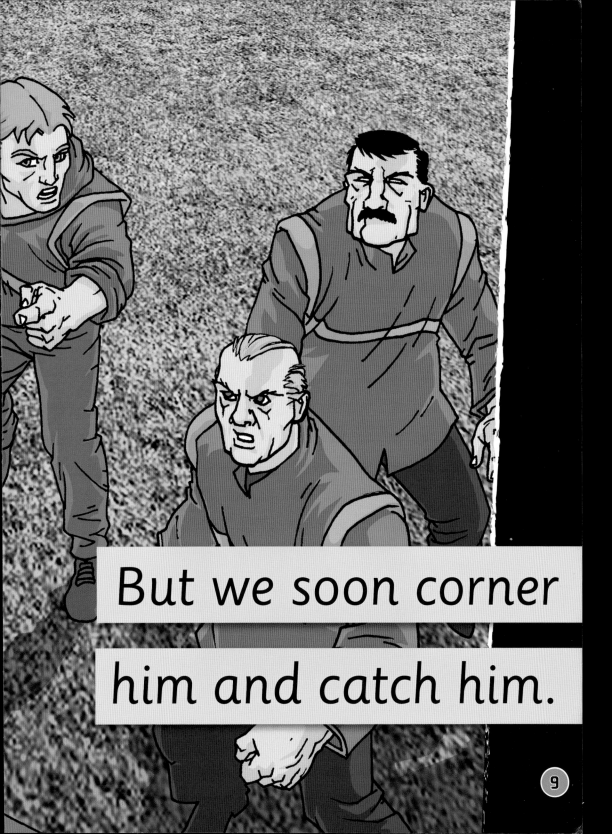

But we soon corner him and catch him.

9

We put him in an arm lock and march him towards the exit.

The crowd begins to hiss and boo and chucks things at him. I put my arm up high and act cool, but I do not feel it!

11

The goalkeeper runs back onto the pitch and the crowd cheers.

But then, a quick shot and the ball is in the net. Is it a goal?

The crowd turns bad and rush to get on the pitch. We begin to panic but cannot show it! Yes! We keep them back!

The match ends and I rush home. With a sigh, I fall down into my arm chair, put my feet up and turn down the lights.

At last, I can see the game.